CHART HI

AUDITION SONGS

WISE PUBLICATIONS
PART OF THE MUSIC SALES GROUP
LONDON / NEW YORK / PARIS / SYDNEY / COPENHAGEN / BERLIN / MADRID / HONG KONG / TOKYO

Published by
WISE PUBLICATIONS
14-15 Berners Street, London W1T 3LJ, UK.

Exclusive Distributors:
MUSIC SALES LIMITED
Distribution Centre, Newmarket Road,
Bury St Edmunds, Suffolk IP33 3YB, UK.
MUSIC SALES PTY LIMITED
20 Resolution Drive,
Caringbah, NSW 2229, Australia.

Order No. AM1002166
ISBN 978-1-84938-816-0
This book © Copyright 2010 Wise Publications,
a division of Music Sales Limited.

Music edited by Jenni Wheeler
Printed in the EU

CD recorded, mixed and mastered by Jonas Persson
Backing tracks arranged by Paul Honey

Your Guarantee of Quality:
As publishers, we strive to produce every book
to the highest commercial standards.
The music has been freshly engraved and the book has
been carefully designed to minimise awkward page turns
and to make playing from it a real pleasure.
Particular care has been given to specifying acid-free,
neutral-sized paper made from pulps which have not been
elemental chlorine bleached.
This pulp is from farmed sustainable forests and was
produced with special regard for the environment.
Throughout, the printing and binding have been planned
to ensure a sturdy, attractive publication which should give
years of enjoyment.
If your copy fails to meet our high standards, please
inform us and we will gladly replace it.

www.musicsales.com

ALL NIGHT LONG
ALEXANDRA BURKE
MUSIC PAGE 12 / CD TRACK 2

BAD ROMANCE
LADY GAGA
MUSIC PAGE 4 / CD TRACK 1

**EMPIRE STATE OF MIND
(PART II) BROKEN DOWN**
ALICIA KEYS
MUSIC PAGE 19 / CD TRACK 3

THE FEAR
LILY ALLEN
MUSIC PAGE 24 / CD TRACK 4

FIGHT FOR THIS LOVE
CHERYL COLE
MUSIC PAGE 30 / CD TRACK 5

HALO
BEYONCÉ
MUSIC PAGE 44 / CD TRACK 7

MAMMA DO
PIXIE LOTT
MUSIC PAGE 50 / CD TRACK 8

RUDE BOY
RIHANNA
MUSIC PAGE 37 / CD TRACK 6

BAD ROMANCE
WORDS & MUSIC BY STEFANI GERMANOTTA & REDONE

5

11

ALL NIGHT LONG

WORDS & MUSIC BY RICO LOVE, JAMES SCHEFFER, SAMUEL WATTERS & LOUIS BIANCANIELLO

1. I see ev-'ry-bod - y a-round___ but it feels like we're in pri - vate.___ (Ooh.)___
(2.)-night the ad-mis-sion is free.___ Now we're shut-tin' the club___ down. (Ooh.)___

13

14

EMPIRE STATE OF MIND (PART II) BROKEN DOWN

WORDS & MUSIC BY ALICIA KEYS, SYLVIA ROBINSON, SHAWN CARTER, ANGELA HUNTE, BERT KEYES, ALEXANDER SHUCKBURGH & JANET SEWELL

Noise is al - ways loud;___ there are si - rens all___ a - round,___ and the streets are mean.___
Such a melt - ing pot;___ on the cor - ner sell - ing rock;___ preach - ers pray to God.___

If I can make___ it here,___ I can make it an - y - where;___ that's what___ they say.___
Hail a gyp - sy cab;___ takes me down from Har - lem to_____ the Brook - lyn Bridge.___

Bmaj7
C♯
4fr
F♯
See-ing my face in lights, or my name in mar-quees found down on Broad-way.
Some-one sleeps at night with a hun-ger for more than an emp-ty fridge.
Bmaj7
C♯
4fr
A♯
6fr
E-ven if it ain't all it seems, I got a pock-et-ful of dreams; ba-by, I'm from
I'm-a make it by an-y means; I got a pock-et-ful of dreams, ba-by, I'm from
New

One hand in the air for The Big Cit-y! Street-lights, big dreams all look-ing pret-ty.

No place in the world that could com-pare. Put your light-ers in the air! Ev-'ry-bod-y say,—

D.S. al Coda

yeah,_____ yeah!_____ Yeah,_____ yeah!__ New__

Coda

__ York!_____

THE FEAR

WORDS & MUSIC BY LILY ALLEN & GREG KURSTIN

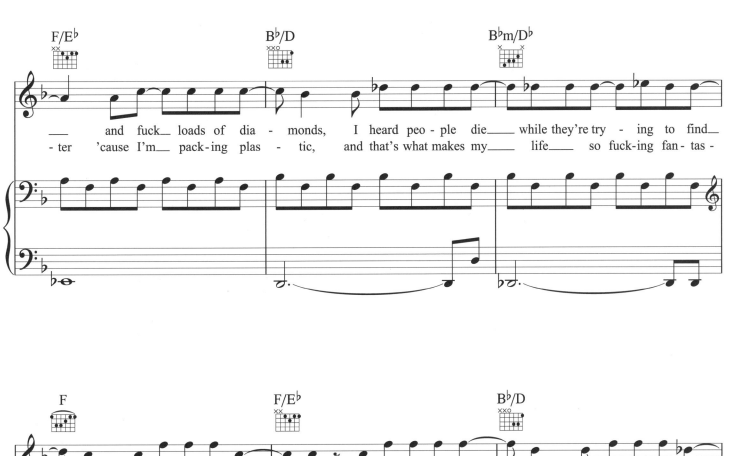

and fuck loads of dia - monds, I heard peo - ple die___ while they're try - ing to find___
- ter 'cause I'm___ pack - ing plas - tic, and that's what makes my___ life___ so fuck - ing fan - tas -

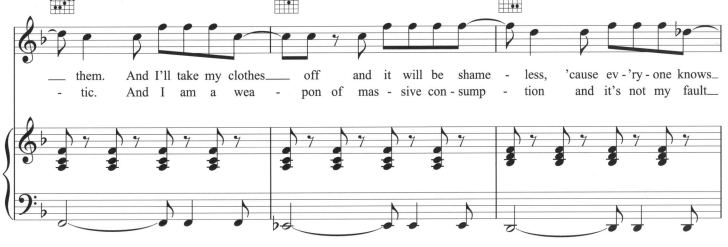

___ them. And I'll take my clothes___ off and it will be shame - less, 'cause ev - 'ry - one knows___
- tic. And I am a wea - pon of mas - sive con - sump - tion and it's not my fault___

___ it's how___ you get fam - ous. I'll look at the Sun___ and I'll look___ in the Mir -
___ it's how I'm pro - grammed to func - tion.___ I'll look at the Sun___ and I'll look___ in the Mir -

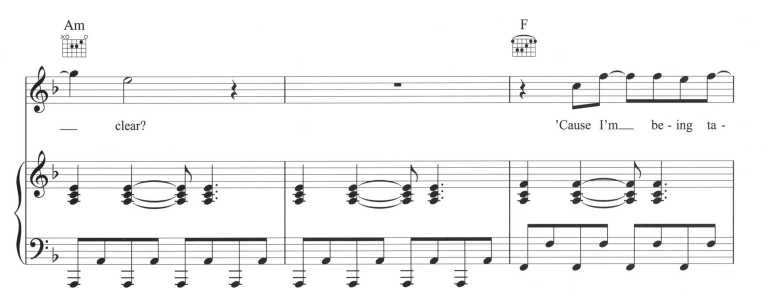

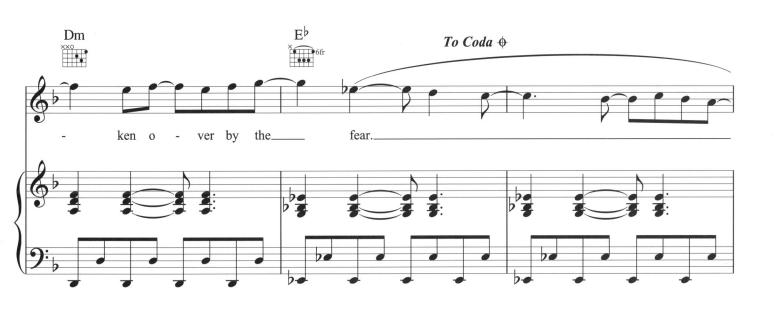

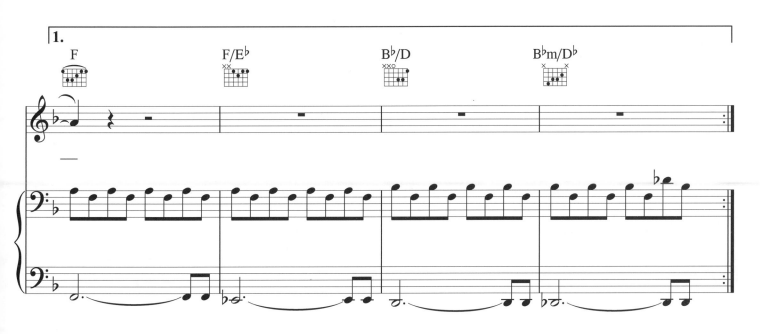

Forget about guns and forget ammunition, 'cause I'm killing them all on my own little mission. Now, I'm not a saint,

FIGHT FOR THIS LOVE

WORDS & MUSIC BY STEVE KIPNER, WAYNE WILKINS
& ANDRE MERRITT

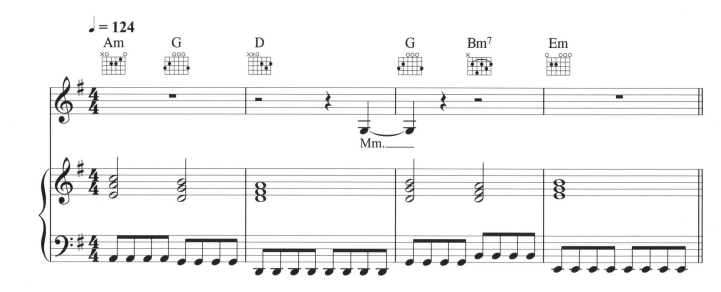

34

RUDE BOY

WORDS & MUSIC BY MIKKEL S. ERIKSEN, TOR ERIK HERMANSEN, ESTHER DEAN, MAKEBA RIDDICK, ROB SWIRE & ROBYN FENTY

HALO

WORDS & MUSIC BY RYAN TEDDER, BEYONCÉ KNOWLES & EVAN BOGART

44

45

MAMA DO

WORDS & MUSIC BY PHIL THORNALLEY & MADS HAUGE

CD TRACK LISTING

BAD ROMANCE
LADY GAGA
CD TRACK 1
(LOVE/SCHEFFER/WATTERS/BIANCANIELLO) EMI MUSIC PUBLISHING LIMITED /
SONY/ATV MUSIC PUBLISHING

ALL NIGHT LONG
ALEXANDRA BURKE
CD TRACK 2
(YESTON) CHERRY LANE MUSIC LIMITED

EMPIRE STATE OF MIND (PART II) BROKEN DOWN
ALICIA KEYS
CD TRACK 3
(KEYS/ROBINSON/CARTER/HUNTE/KEYES/SHUCKBURGH/SEWELL) EMI MUSIC PUBLISHING LIMITED /
IQ MUSIC LIMITED / GLOBAL TALENT PUBLISHING

THE FEAR
LILY ALLEN
CD TRACK 4
(ALLEN/KURSTIN) UNIVERSAL MUSIC PUBLISHING LIMITED / EMI MUSIC PUBLISHING LIMITED

FIGHT FOR THIS LOVE
CHERYL COLE
CD TRACK 5
(KIPNER/WILKINS/MERRITT) SONY/ATV MUSIC PUBLISHING / EMI MUSIC PUBLISHING LIMITED /
UNIVERSAL MUSIC PUBLISHING LIMITED / UNIVERSAL/MCA MUSIC LIMITED

RUDE BOY
RIHANNA
CD TRACK 6
(ERIKSEN/HERMANSEN/RIDDICK/DEAN/SWIRE/FENTY) EMI MUSIC PUBLISHING LIMITED /
PEERMUSIC (UK) LIMITED / CHRYSALIS MUSIC LIMITED

HALO
BEYONCÉ
CD TRACK 7
(TEDDER/KNOWLES/BOGART) KOBALT MUSIC PUBLISHING LIMITED / SONY/ATV MUSIC PUBLISH
EMI MUSIC PUBLISHING LIMITED

MAMA DO
PIXIE LOTT
CD TRACK 8
(THORNALLEY/HAUGE) UNIVERSAL MUSIC PUBLISHING MGB LIMITED